DATE DUE

DEC 1 3 '93			

DEMCO 38-297

The Hawaiian Way

The Hawaiian Way

by Wilma Pitchford Hays

illustrated by Charles G. Chu

Coward-McCann, Inc.
New York

4

To
EVERY BOY AND GIRL

who wants to know
how other children live
and what they believe

CONTENTS

Foreword
PEACE THROUGH UNDERSTANDING

WHEN Hawaii became the fiftieth state, it brought into the Union many different kinds of people who were experienced in living with a variety of religious beliefs and national backgrounds.

For hundreds of years the islands of Hawaii in the Pacific Ocean have been a stopping place for ships from many parts of the world. From China and Japan, men brought to Hawaii the ways of the East: Buddhism and Confucianism. From America and Europe, men brought Judaism and Protestant and Catholic Christianity. With friendly hospitality the native Hawaiians welcomed each group of people. Men and women from the various countries remained in Hawaii and are now Americans.

The islands of Hawaii are small and far from the mainland, so the many kinds of people living there grew to know each other as neighbors do. The children from different nations and religions grew up together, attended school and played together. When the children became men and women and worked side by side in business and government, they paid much less attention to their cultural differences than their parents and grandparents had done.

They had learned that the most important part of a person is what he *thinks* and *believes,* for these determine what he *does.* They found that the knowledge of other religions and ways of life did not make a person turn away from his own beliefs, but helped him to understand his neighbors better. And they discovered that they did not need to *look* alike or *think* alike in order to trust one another.

This experience of different kinds of people in living together is the greatest gift which the new state brought into the United States. The following chapters are stories about boys in Hawaii and something about what each boy believes. Added together, the chapters form a picture of *The Hawaiian Way* of life.

W. P. H.

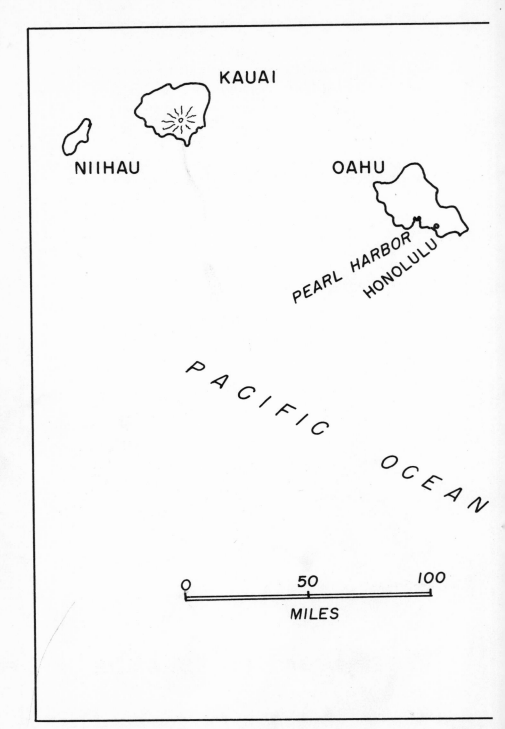

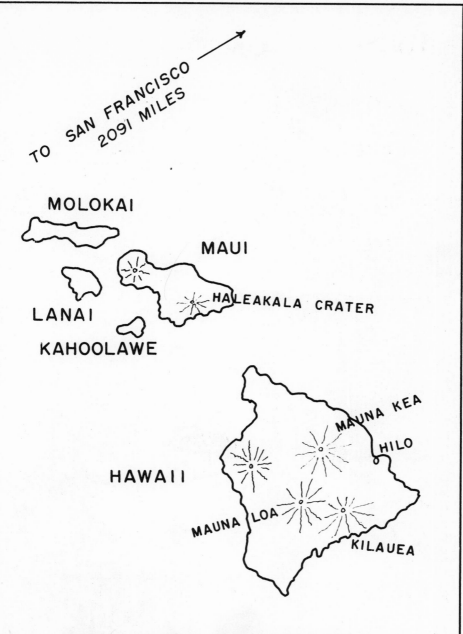

TO SAN FRANCISCO 2091 MILES

MOLOKAI

MAUI

LANAI

KAHOOLAWE

HALEAKALA CRATER

MAUNA KEA

HILO

HAWAII

MAUNA LOA

KILAUEA

THE HAWAIIAN ISLANDS

JOHN AKAKA

John Akaka—native Hawaiian, Protestant. He lives on the big island of Hawaii, in a small village near the coast below the city of Hilo.

WITH his arms full of fragrant white and yellow flowers, John Akaka walked into the church where his grandmother was getting ready for a meeting of the Hawaiian Women's Missionary Society. He found her polishing the wood altar.

"Are these enough flowers?" he asked.

His grandmother turned. Her short gray hair curled about a brown face too full to wrinkle, and her smile was as gay as her flowered dress.

"Mahalo nui, thank you very much, Johnny," she said. "Now please pump some water into the tall white vases. Be careful not to spill it in the aisle. I want everything just right for the meeting."

John grinned as he carried the vases to the outdoor pump. His grandmother was very proud of being a descendant of the first Hawaiians to be taught Christianity by the missionary haoles, white men, from New England. She loved this old church which her people had helped the missionaries build when she was a girl. She liked to tell John and his younger sister, Ruth, about the happy times when she was young.

Long ago, she had said, Hawaiian men, women and children worked together to build the church. Some people cut lava rock, some cut trees, some mixed coarse coral sand for mortar.

They sang as they worked. When the native Hawaiians were tired, they stopped to eat together from wooden bowls of poi made from pounded taro root. They ate small sweet bananas and coconuts and mangoes from their trees, fish and eel from the sea. The Hawaiians never hurried their meals but took time for laughter and talk and to play with their children.

In the hot afternoons everyone would nap under the shade of a spreading hau or monkeypod tree. Sometimes when they woke, they baffled the hard-working haole missionaries by deciding to go for a swim. Or when a cool trade wind came from the sea, they might stop work for a whole day of hula dancing.

With hibiscus blooms or orchids in their hair or behind an ear or strung in leis about their necks or worn in crowns upon their heads, the native Hawaiians would sing and dance the old folk hulas of their ancestors. Many of their graceful hulas were prayer dances which they used to perform to please the goddess Pele. After becoming Christians, the gay Hawaiians danced their folk hulas just as enthusiastically to honor God.

John was glad that even now on special days, at a luau feast or a hukilau, a pull-net fishing party, his family and friends gathered together to sing the old songs and dance the old hulas. He always wanted to remember the ways of his people.

As John pumped water into the white vases, he felt the earth move under his feet. He stopped pumping and stood very still.

Again the earth shook and there was a dull rumble. The air smelled of sulphur. A cat streaked across the churchyard and raced down the slope toward the sea. Every hair on its tail stood straight out, stiff as a bottle brush.

John couldn't help laughing although he realized now what was happening. The volcano Kilauea must be erupting again. Although Kilauea was fifteen miles away, it had sent cinders and smoke over the village many times during the past two months. Once the smoke had been so dense that school had to be dismissed and the children were sent to the beach where they could breath more easily.

No one had minded *that,* John thought. In fact everyone was excited and eager to watch the show the volcano put on. Visitors came by planes from Honolulu and from all the other islands to see the roaring fountain of lava spout from the mountain. The only live volcanoes in Hawaii were on the Big Island and it might be years before one would become active again.

John saw a big Hawaiian fisherman climbing the slope past the church. The earth shook again and the fisherman waved.

"Pele really hu-hu, angry, tonight," he shouted.

John looked at the wide cloud of black smoke moving toward him from the moutain and his neck prickled. Not that he really believed in the ancient goddess Pele, whom his ancestors had worshiped. Still, when the volcano blazed and rumbled, he couldn't help remembering the tales his grandmother had told him about Pele, the goddess of fire.

For more than a thousand years Hawaiians had believed that the goddess Pele lived in a lake of fire in the pit of Kilauea. They had sacrificed to her and worshiped her so that Pele would not destroy them and their homes in her angry outbursts.

When the mountain smoked and rumbled, the terrified Hawaiians would try to appease Pele. To satisfy Pele and keep some disaster from falling upon them, many of the old Hawaiians had knocked out their front teeth, tattooed their tongues and burned patches of skin from their bodies. If a member of the royal family, the Alii, was very ill or died, the people had even offered human sacrifices at the pit of Kilauea.

Then with the coming of the Congregational Missionaries from New England to Hawaii more than a hundred years ago, the native Hawaiians had learned of the God of love. The missionary haoles told the Hawaiians that the Christian God loved *men.* He was not pleased when they harmed themselves or sacrificed things to Him.

They said that God had sent His Son, Jesus, to be born into the world to teach men to love one another and do unto others as they would have done unto them.

The message of a God of love, who urged all men to treat others as brothers, appealed to the friendly Hawaiians. Some of them began to believe in God and Jesus.

One of these believers was a Hawaiian queen named Kapiolani, who lived near Hilo. She had worshiped Pele all her life until the missionary haoles came. Kapiolani was quick to learn and to believe in the one true God. She was sorry that many of her people were so afraid of Pele that they dared not become Christians.

One day she said that she was going to climb the volcano Kilauea and enter the crater itself which was kapu, forbidden. Her trembling people begged her not to go, saying that she would be destroyed and they would all be harmed if she insulted Pele. The crater of Kilauea was sacred to the goddess of fire.

Kapiolani answered her people, "If I am destroyed, then believe in Pele. If I enter the crater and live, you will know that Pele has no power. You can believe in the true God without fear."

Many of the people followed Kapiolani on her long climb up the mountain. When she descended into the pit where flames spat and leaped in a lake of fire and the earth trembled, most of her followers ran away. Others covered their faces. They expected the lava crust to open up and swallow Kapiolani.

Kapiolani flung rocks into the flames and called upon Pele to show her anger. Then she knelt and offered a prayer to God right on the brink of Pele's lava lake.

After Kapiolani's brave act, most of her followers were no longer afraid of the fire goddess. They tore down their old temples and stopped worshiping the red-colored rock which was the symbol of Pele. Thirty thousand Hawaiians became Christians within a few years.

John heard his grandmother calling him. "Where is the water? The flowers are wilting."

He finished filling the white vases and took them into the

church. "Kilauea is erupting again," he said. "I hope the smoke doesn't spoil your meeting."

As he helped his grandmother arrange the flowers in the vases, he heard someone running up the steps into the church.

"John — Grandma," his sister Ruth cried. "Come quick. A volcano spouting—" She had to stop to catch her breath.

John grinned at his sister. "You ought to be used to Kilauea by now," he said.

"Not Kilauea," she cried. "A new eruption. The earth cracked and opened in the sugar-cane field not half a mile above the town."

John saw his grandmother back up to the old polished wood altar as if her ample bulk could shield it from the lava flow nearby.

"How do you know?" he asked Ruth.

"I was in Papa's store when the men came to telephone," Ruth said.

John nodded. Their father's small grocery store had a public telephone.

"Men are here from the Hawaiian Observatory and from Civil Defense," Ruth said. "They say there is a crack of fire in the field, almost two miles long. And some of the fountains are three hundred feet high."

John coughed and his eyes began to smart. Smoke was rolling into the church. "Come on, Grandma, we can't stay here," he said.

"Papa says we have to leave the town," Ruth said. "We are to go to Aunt Mary's in Hilo." She ran ahead of John.

Halfway down the aisle, John turned to see if his grandmother was coming. He saw her lifting the heavy Bible from the altar. She wanted to save it if anything should happen to the church.

John waited for her. He knew how she felt. He loved this church, too. It was like a second home to him.

Before this altar he had been baptized. Here he had learned to sing hymns like "Jesus loves me, this I know, for the Bible tells me so." Only last Sunday he had received his own Bible as a gift. Written on the front page in the minister's hand was, *To John Akaka, for faithful attendance at Sunday School.*

In Sunday school he had learned verses from the Bible, the Lord's Prayer, the Ten Commandments, the Beatitudes, and the psalm which began, "The Lord is my shepherd, I shall not want."

He had taken part in the pageants and services at Christmas and Easter. Christmas told of the birth of the child Jesus in a manger when shepherds, lead by a star, came to worship Him and angels sang for joy. Easter told of the man Jesus, Lord and teacher, who rose from death after the mob had crucified Him on a cross. And Jesus had promised that all people who loved God would live again as He did.

John saw his grandmother come down the aisle carrying the altar Bible in both arms. He followed her from the church.

Rain was falling. The evening sky was already dark with storm clouds and smoke. John took off his yellow print shirt and tucked it about the Bible to keep it dry. Then he hurried beside his grandmother down the slope to his father's store in the village.

The little wooden building was jammed with men and women and children. Each child had an all-day sucker and seemed to be enjoying the excitement.

A ranger from the National Volcano Park came into the store and raised his hand for attention. "Will you all go home and pack your clothing?" he said pleasantly. "We will have cars here in the morning to move the women and children from the town."

There was a buzz of talk and he raised his voice. "We expect the lava to flow north of us into the sea. But we will get a lot of cinders and smoke here. And if the flow *should* turn toward the town, we don't want anyone here except the men who can help with the moving and with fighting fires."

The people pushed out of the store to go to their homes. John wanted to stay and help the men work, but his father said that his mother would need him. He went home with Ruth and his grandmother.

His mother was already packing. When the suitcases and boxes were filled, she said they must all go to bed and get some rest before time to leave in the morning.

John lay down with his clothes on but he could not sleep. He could hear the rumble and roar of the volcano behind the town. Through his windows, he saw the dull red glare of the fountains of lava shooting into the sky. He heard trucks moving back and forth along the village streets and men calling directions.

He must have fallen asleep finally. He woke to find his bed shaking violently. He sat up quickly. Only a big quake could shake the earth like that.

His grandmother came into his room. "We are all awake," she said, "so let's have breakfast."

John slid off his bed and ran to the window. By the early-morning light, he saw men on bulldozers pushing the rocky soil into a long high wall behind the town. He knew they hoped this dike would turn the lava toward the sea. He saw crews from the Hawaii Electric Company climbing poles and winding cable to save it from burning.

He turned to his grandmother. "Grandma," he said, "do you think the lava will reach our town and burn the houses and the church and everything?"

She came to the window and stood beside him. "I don't know whether we will lose our homes and the church or not," she said. "But we must not fear. God is everywhere. He loves us and will help us wherever we go."

John was thoughtful. He knew that God loved every person as a father loves his child. Jesus cared what happened to people, too, and He wanted men to help each other. John thought of the men who had come from many miles around to help their neighbors in the town. He felt better.

"Grandma," he said, "I guess I *am* hungry enough to eat breakfast."

DANNY O'BRIEN

Danny O'Brien—Irish-English-Hawaiian Catholic. He lives on the island of Maui in the small town of Lahaina, until 1843 national capital of the kingdom of Hawaii.

DANNY O'BRIEN sat on the wharf at the old waterfront of Lahaina and dangled his bare feet in the warm water of the harbor. The sun shone hot on his wide coconut hat and on the red print aloha shirt he wore with his swimming trunks. The little town seemed deserted except for two dusky boys who napped under the banyan tree which spread on its many trunks like a great green circus top.

Then Danny saw the tour-bus he had been waiting for. The bus pulled up and stopped near a weather-beaten storeroom on a corner of the waterfront. Danny scrambled to his feet and ran across the dusty square to meet the driver.

"Harry," Danny called to the big Hawaiian stepping from the bus, "I was afraid you weren't coming this morning and I wouldn't get to see the divers' movie today."

The friendly bus driver grinned. "How many times you see that movie?" he teased. "Maui divers gonna charge you admission this time — sure!"

Danny smiled and walked into the Maui Divers' Shop with the big Hawaiian. A flock of tourists from the bus followed and began to exclaim over the display of lacy black coral trees and the jewelry which had been hand-fashioned from the rare black coral. He waited as patiently as he could while women tried on earrings and necklaces. At last the driver invited all the visitors to come into the workroom behind the shop, where the Maui divers would show a movie they had taken of their own work underwater where the black coral trees grew.

Danny was the first one into the workroom. He went straight to a keg in front of the battered movie screen where he could see every move in the pictures he knew so well.

When the visitors had seated themselves on old chests or wooden chairs, the electric light was turned out. In the dusk one of the divers began to focus the jumpy colored movie until it grew clear. Then he told a story as he showed the pictures.

He said that he and two other professional divers had been aqualung fishing between the islands of Maui and Lanai when they discovered an undersea forest of rare black coral trees. The trees grew as high as twenty feet and as wide as a hibiscus bush. Their strong coral trunks were rooted on white coral cliffs about two hundred feet underwater.

In the movie, Danny saw one of his diver friends hacking at a coral root with a chisel. The root clung like a barnacle to the rocky edge surrounding the black mouth of an undersea cave.

Danny had seen this movie a hundred times but a shiver always raced up his spine as he watched the strange dim underwater world. He wanted to be a diver when he grew up, and he hoped he would be as fearless as the Maui divers.

Danny saw the deep undercurrents of the sea tug at the bubbling fishman who was hacking at the root of the coral tree. The water floated the diver's body so that he could put little strength behind his blows to pry the tree from its hold on the rock cliff.

Colorful fish swam about the diver. The long dark shadow of a shark swam below him. But Danny knew that sharks and undercurrents were not the real dangers of diving.

The real danger was "the bends," which could bring death. At the depth where black coral grew, a diver would get nitrogen bubbles in his blood if he surfaced too quickly.

Each diver wore a bottle of air strapped to his packboard. If the diver failed to hack off the coral tree in three minutes, he must give up and begin a slow trip to the surface with short stops for decompression. If he worked longer than three minutes, he would not have enough air remaining in his bottle to allow him eight minutes for a safe return.

Danny knew he was only watching a movie and that the divers had returned safely, yet his heart beat faster as the seconds ticked by. The diver had been down three minutes, but he still hacked at the stubborn coral root. It was easy to understand why a diver hated to give up until he had his tree. Two dives a day were all that a man could make safely. And these dives must be made at the tide change when, for about an hour, the powerful undercurrents slackened.

At the last possible moment of safety, Danny saw the root of the coral tree give way under the diver's chisel. Quickly the diver tied a rope about the coral trunk below its lacy branches. Danny knew that a yellow float was attached to the other end of the rope on the water's surface. The coral tree would be hauled up and taken aboard the diver's open-decked boat.

As the diver on the movie screen began to make his bubbling way to the surface, Danny heard a murmur of appreciation from the watching tourists. The lights went on in the workroom. With the group of visitors, Danny made his way through the shop into the sunlight on the street.

He glanced toward the harbor, where fishing sampans and small sailboats rested inside the lava rock breakwater. There was the yellow bow of the Maui divers' eighteen-foot motorboat. He saw his diver friends, Larry and Jack, loading gear.

They must be taking off for the black coral beds. Danny ran toward the harbor. Before he reached the men, he heard the outboard motors rev and saw the divers cast off the mooring ropes. The yellow boat moved out of the harbor.

Danny stopped and watched the boat buck the foaming surf until it reached deep blue-green waters far out to sea. The spell of the movie was still so strong upon him that he was worried

23

about the dangers his diver friends were facing again. He touched the St. Christopher's medal he wore on a thin chain around his neck and made a prayer to the saint to give strength and protection to the divers while they worked.

Still Danny felt troubled. He was not sure that St. Christopher would listen to him after what he had done yesterday. He had taken two large ripe mangoes from the convent garden and had run away when Sister Superior called him to come to her. He hadn't yet gone to confession or done penance for his wrongdoing.

Something made Danny want to go to the church and light a prayer candle for each of his diver friends. He had earned the money to pay for the candles by helping weed the field of carnations his father grew to sell to florists and lei makers.

The church was always open so that anyone who felt troubled could enter and seek God. At the door of the church Danny dipped his fingers into a font of water blessed by the priest. He made the sign of the cross, touching his forehead, shoulders and waist and saying, "In the name of the Father and of the Son and of the Holy Ghost."

As he faced the altar and touched his knee to the floor in adoration, he saw the ever-burning sanctuary lamp and, above it, a crucifix of Christ upon the Cross. Danny was the only person in the church at this hour. In the cool, dim quiet, he entered a pew and knelt and remembered the many times he had heard Mass here.

The sisters had taught him in school that the center aisle leading to the steps of the altar was a symbol of the pathway to God Himself. And the Mass was a celebration of the last supper which God's Son, Jesus the Christ, ate with his disciples. In every Mass, Jesus sacrificed Himself again to save all those who repented their sins and hoped to live with Him in Heaven. Danny believed that when he received Holy Communion the bread and wine were changed into the body and blood of Christ and he actually received Christ, his Saviour.

Danny left the pew and lighted three votive candles at a

side altar. He prayed to St. Christopher and to the Holy Mother to protect his diver friends. As he left the church and crossed himself again with the holy water at the font, Danny felt better. He knew that the candles would burn for hours. He believed that as long as they burned the candles would carry his prayer to Heaven, where God and Jesus and St. Christopher and the Holy Mother would hear it.

Danny was hungry and went home to lunch. His younger brother and three sisters were already eating at a table on the lanai, the porch, overlooking the garden behind the house. They told Danny that their father had been looking for him to help in the carnation field. A large order had come from lei makers in Honolulu for carnations which must be flown out on the afternoon plane.

Danny's mother, wearing a cool blue flowered muumuu, an unbelted dress, brought him a wooden bowl of poi and a piece of fish, fried crisply brown but flaky-white inside. For dessert he had a quarter wedge of fresh ripe pineapple.

His uncle, who worked for one of the big canning companies, had brought home several large choice fruits from the pineapple field. Danny took the sweet juicy wedge to the shade of a banana tree in the garden and ate it as he would eat watermelon, with the juice dripping onto the ground.

"Better hurry," his mother called. "Your father needs you to help cut carnations."

Danny worked for several hours among the rows of red carnations in his father's field. He was used to the heat of the sun. His coconut hat protected his head. A breeze from the sea cooled him now and then when he stood up to rest his back. And he loved the cinnamony fragrance of the red blooms.

On his way home that evening, Danny saw a group of men, women and children gathered on the wharf. The sampans were back from fishing and most of the sailboats had returned to harbor. But he sensed an unusual excitement there.

Danny began to run. As he neared the harbor, he looked for the divers' yellow boat, but it was nowhere to be seen. He

25

joined a group of people who were listening to the captain of a sailboat which had come in from the sea.

"I tell you, it couldn't happen again in a million years," the captain was saying. "It's fantastic that a man could be so near death and be saved by such a run of luck and pure chance."

Danny called over the heads of the taller people in front of him. "Who was hurt? Was it one of the divers?"

Two boys left the crowd and joined Danny. They were his friends Jim Kawamoto and David Livingston.

"Larry had an accident underwater," David said.

Jim interrupted. "Larry was working the coral beds when the strap holding his air bottle broke, and jerked the air hose right out of his mouth. He swam after the bottle and caught it."

"But," David cut in, "so much air had escaped that Larry had to come up fast without decompressing. When Jack pulled him into the boat, Larry felt woozy. He took another bottle of air and dived again, hoping to decompress. But when he came back up, he sat down in the back of the boat and passed out."

"And guess what?" Jim cried.

"Is Larry all right?" Danny asked. "Where is he now?"

"You're not going to believe this," David said, "but we heard the captain of the sailboat tell it, so it must be true. You know there's no decompression chamber nearer than Pearl Harbor, and that's hours away. It looked as if Larry was a goner.

"Then Jack saw a ship traveling across the water. He raced toward the ship as fast as his motorboat could go. On the way he gave Larry mouth-to-mouth resuscitation."

David paused for breath and Jim took up the story. "The ship turned out to be a U. S. submarine rescue ship! It had a decompression chamber on board. But that's not all. That ship carried a medical officer who was an expert on the bends. The officer put Larry into a decompression chamber and took him to Pearl Harbor for treatment."

"And," David cried, "the doctor said Larry wouldn't be

alive now if that ship hadn't been right there. Larry will have to be in a hospital a long time, but he sure is lucky."

Danny looked at his two friends. He was so relieved to hear that Larry was alive that he couldn't speak. Beneath his aloha shirt he felt the touch of the St. Christopher medal against his breastbone. He thought of the prayer candles he had lighted in the church at noon. Then he looked thoughtfully out to sea where the divers had met a rescue ship at the very moment when Larry had to have help to save his life. Danny felt sure that his prayers had been heard.

ELI RUBIN

*Eli Rubin—Hungarian Jewish.
A year ago he was adopted by
Mr. and Mrs. Max Rubin,
owners of a clothing store in
Honolulu on the Island of Oahu.*

ELI RUBIN leaned against the wire fence which edged
a landing strip of the Honolulu airport and watched for the
two-motored planes due from the nearby islands. His new
father had invited relatives and friends from Kauai, Maui,
Molokai and Hawaii, for Eli's Bar Mitzvah tomorrow.

Eli frowned to find himself still thinking of Max Rubin as
his *new* father. He knew that the kind man and woman who
had adopted him a year ago wanted him to forget that he had
lived in a displaced persons' camp after he had lost his family
in an escape from Hungary. Mr. and Mrs. Rubin wanted him
to think of them as his father and mother now, and their baby
Sarah as his sister. He must try to remember.

A United States Army training plane roared overhead on
its way to Hickam Field. Eli ducked and covered his face with
his arms. A moment later he dropped his hands to his side and
hoped that no one had noticed his instinctive fright. He must
learn not to fear bomber planes any more.

He lived in peaceful Hawaii now. Airplane hopping was
the common way in which people went about from island to
island. Eli heard a woman tourist near him say to another,
"I can't get used to it. These Hawaiians take planes the way
we take buses on the mainland."

Overhead Eli saw two planes coming in from different directions. Like giant seagulls they swooped down on the landing field, seconds apart. Steps unfolded from their sides and people poured out and surged toward the gates. Eli watched eagerly for the one person he would recognize, his new father's sister, Aunt Reba. He hadn't met the other relatives coming today.

Most of the men and women and children leaving the planes wore casual dress, muumuus or aloha shirts and slacks. Almost everyone carried gifts for friends, packages and leis or bouquets of brilliant flowers. Three young Hawaiian men, each with a hibiscus blossom behind an ear, were singing and grinning while one of them strummed on a ukulele.

Eli smiled. One couldn't stay frightened very long among the gay Hawaiian people.

Then he saw Aunt Reba, slim in a blue dress with a pretty flowered hat on her dark hair. An older woman was with her. Eli knew that they had both dressed well in honor of this important time when he would become Bar Mitzvah, a Son of the Commandment. After this day he would be responsible for his own behavior. He would fast and pray and go to the synagogue just as the men did.

Aunt Reba saw him and waved. Eli hurried to the gate to meet her. She hugged him and kissed him on both cheeks. "Eli, this is your father's aunt from Kona," Aunt Reba said. Eli was gathered into plump arms and kissed and hugged again, just as if this stranger was his *real* aunt.

"Father sent the car for you," Eli said. "He was so busy getting ready for tomorrow."

"We know," Aunt Reba said fondly. "Bar Mitzvah. Such an important day for a boy—for his whole family, too."

By late afternoon twelve relatives had gathered in the Rubin home. Eli saw that the travelers had hung their leis everywhere, even over the shades of the floor lamps. The grandmother, on his new mother's side, was crooning to Sarah, as if a baby could go to sleep with all that chatter coming from the kitchen. The women were so busy preparing the Sabbath supper and the

30

extra food for celebration after the Bar Mitzvah service tomorrow, that no one noticed how quiet Eli was.

With all the excited talk around him, Eli was homesick for the sound of more familiar language. He had learned English quickly and almost never broke into Hungarian any more. He understood everything said to him and he spoke with only a slight accent, but English was still a strange language to him.

He saw Aunt Reba hurry to the table on the lanai and place the twisted Sabbath loaves, hallah, on the white tablecloth beside the silver candlesticks. His new mother would soon light the candles in the age-old ceremony that ushers in the Sabbath.

Eli remembered the sunset hour of Friday evenings in his home in Hungary before the revolution. He had stood with his father and mother and older brother before the table. His mother had spread her hands above the candle flame, then held them before her face as she prayed in Hebrew, the ancient language of the Jewish people.

"Blesed art Thou, O Lord our God, King of the universe, Who hast sanctified us by Thy commandments, and commanded us to kindle the Sabbath lights.
May our home be consecrated, O God, by Thy Light."

In spite of the gay talk and laughter during supper and the presents given to him, Eli couldn't overcome his feeling of homesickness. These friendly strange people weren't his real family.

The next morning when all Eli's new family proudly entered the synagogue with him, he was still homesick. He sat in a pew beside his new father. They were early. Eli could look around without seeming to stare.

On a platform at the front of the room was the reading desk where the Cantor was testing a reading lamp. Eli saw the Sacred Ark, a cabinet covered with a velvet curtain embroidered with a six-pointed star, the Shield of David. He knew that inside the Ark was the Torah from which the Cantor would read. Before the Ark hung the lamp which was never allowed to go out, the Eternal Light.

31

In this quiet house of God, Eli's heart began to beat fast. Would he remember all that the Rabbi and his new father had taught him in preparation for this day? Sometimes when a Bar Mitzvah boy went forward to read his portion from the Torah, he was asked a few questions to answer before all the people. Silently Eli rehearsed some of the things he was expected to know:

Jewish people must be good citizens of any country in which they live. They must feel themselves united only in their ways of worship, which they have followed for many many generations no matter where they lived.

The first Hebrew, Abraham, was father of the Jews, but Moses was their great leader and teacher. Moses led the Jews from Egypt where the Egyptian king had made them slaves. Moses gave them the Ten Commandments and the law from the One God. Moses taught them that it was wrong to worship idols and false gods as many Hebrews were then doing. He taught them that the One God, Yahweh, was a living, personal God, a God of righteous action. If they obeyed Him, God would act to help them every day in trouble or in joy.

God had called the Jews His chosen people. They were not chosen to be better than other people or to be more privileged, but to do a task. The Jews were to tell all the nations of the world to turn away from worshiping many false gods and to know the One God.

Eli's thoughts were interrupted by the entrance of the Rabbi. The service was about to begin. Eli listened carefully to the singing and the chants and prayers. Then the Cantor turned and took the Torah from the Sacred Ark. Carefully the Cantor unrolled the parchment scroll and placed it on the reading desk. He began to chant and his words were all in Hebrew.

From the time he was small, Eli had studied Hebrew at home and at school. He had heard his father read these words aloud many times. Now, when the reading of the verses and the blessing of each portion were finished, Eli found that he no longer felt as lonely as he had when he came into the synagogue.

He heard the call for the Bar Mitzvah boy to come forward to the reader's desk.

Eli stood and walked up the aisle. The Cantor pointed to the few verses of the Torah which Eli was to read. Eli looked down at the Hebrew words copied carefully by hand on the parchment scroll. The words were ones he had learned in his home in Hungary. He began to read in the ancient language of the Jewish people. "Shema yisroel Adonoy eloheynu Adonoy echod." Hear O Israel: the Lord our God, the Lord is One.

When Eli had finished reading the verses, he found that hearing and speaking Hebrew again had made him feel at home in his new country, as it had helped Jewish people to feel at home for thousands of years no matter where they were scattered in the world.

Eli looked down and saw his father smiling proudly at him. He saw his mother and his Aunt Reba and all the other relatives who had seemed like strangers to him a few hours before. He felt close to them now as if they were his real family. Eli felt good all through as he left the platform and walked down the aisle to sit beside *his* father.

SAM YOSHIDA

*Sam Yoshida—Japanese Shinto.
He lives on the island of Kauai,
the garden isle, most ancient
of the chain of islands which
forms the state of Hawaii.*

SAM YOSHIDA sat in the rickety guard tower in the center of his father's rice patch and watched a flock or rice birds hover above the ripening grain. The birds swept low and settled to eat the rice. With both hands Sam caught the strong lines which stretched above the small field in every direction like the spokes of a wagon wheel. Hung on each line were tin-can lids and old clothes to frighten away the small flying thieves.

Sam pulled the main string in the tower. The lids rattled all across the field. The clothes flapped. The birds rose into the air, scolding as they circled above the grass thatched roof of the tower.

"Go away," Sam shouted. "Papa-san works very hard to make this rice grow. He'll be plenty hu-hu if you eat it."

Sam knew that his grandma-san would be angry, too, if the birds stole the rice. She was proud that her son, Sam's father, still planted rice for her. He had a good job in a nursery in the town and need not grow his own rice, but Grandma-san did not like the rice bought in stores. To make her special rice balls, Grandma-san felt she must have tender rice grown as it had been in Japan years ago before she came to Hawaii to live.

Sam was Japanese in many ways but he was also American

35

and Hawaiian. His English speech was spiced with Hawaiian words and he liked poi as much as he did rice.

Sam attended the public school in the town, where his marks were A's and B's. Each morning he stood proudly with his classmates and pledged allegiance to the flag of the United States of America. And no one sang "The Star-Spangled Banner" with more fervor than Sam sang it now that Hawaii was the fiftieth state.

Yet he was proud of his Japanese ancestry, too. Grandma-san, who lived with his family, had taught Sam the patience to set rice plants underwater by hand in fields flooded above his knees. She had taught him to see beauty in everything about him, to love and serve his country and to respect his parents and teachers.

"Life is good," she had told Sam from the time he was very small. "You need only a few rules to be good, too."

She urged him to try to make his life beautiful. To seek honor. Be loyal. Respect his family and be considerate of all others.

"That is enough," she had said many times, "except, of course, to keep very clean."

Sam thought of Grandma-san now. She was probably making rice balls for supper. The thought made him hungry. He saw that dusk was beginning and the birds were flying away to their roosts. The rice would be safe for the night.

Sam climbed down the ladder from the tower and ran across the field to a winding path which lead from the swampy valley to his home on the mountainside.

A sudden misty rain cooled his face. Looking up he saw a rainbow arched across the sky from the top of the mountain into the blue-green waters of the sea. He stopped and was happy just to watch the rainbow while it faded. He knew that some of his school friends attended churches to hear sermons about a great God. For him, the beauty of this island brought the inspiration and joy which his friends seemed to find in their churches.

Sam's sermons were told in nature, and Grandma-san had taught him how to listen to them. On his left a waterfall tumbled foaming from a crevice in the side of the mountain. It seemed to Sam that this waterfall was Heaven's power sent to earth. The mountain itself was the divine spirit of earth reaching up toward Heaven.

The side of the small canyon cut by the waterfall was almost as colorful as a rainbow. Lush green plants grew along gashes of iron-red earth. Lava rock, worn by centuries of wind and rain and sun, had turned lavender, orange-pink and blue, and the rock colors rivaled the wild flowers growing along the stream below the waterfall.

Below Sam, where steep lava cliffs edged the sea, giant waves rolled in from far across the water. A breaker struck against the cliff, leaped to the top and sent white spray arching backward to meet the next wave rolling in. The deep boom of the surf attacking the rock was like music to Sam. He felt the wonderful forces that moved in nature. And he believed that these same forces moved in him. Nature and he were a part of each other.

He walked along under the trees and felt their nearness to him. He loved the sculptured beauty of the Norway pines and the majestic height of the royal coconut palms.

When he came to the small garden his father had made along the mountain stream which ran behind their home, Sam stopped again. It was almost dark but he could see the vanda orchids growing in clumps as if they were wild, and the hedge of coral-orange bird-of-paradise blooms. Beyond, in a corner of the garden under a golden shower tree, was the small shrine his father had built, for there was no public Shinto shrine near their home.

Sam crossed the garden and paused before the Torri, the special gateway to the shrine. A simple arched roof of wood joined the two upright posts of the gateway.

Sam felt an urge to enter the shrine for a moment. Quickly he washed his feet in the stream, then washed his hands and dipped a palmful of water and rinsed his mouth to cleanse and purify himself before going through the Torii.

Inside the small prayer-hall Sam knelt with his bare feet tucked under him and was quiet.

The sides of the shrine were open to the night. Sam could hear the hum of insects and the sigh of the wind in the golden showers of flowers overhead. He smelled the fragrance of yellow ginger.

A kind of awe came over him in the presence of the beauty here in the garden. He felt that he was a part of the divine spirit that lived in the mountain, the wind, the sea, the red earth and the trees and flowers. He wanted to make his life beautiful, too.

"The divine spirit is in everything," he recited prayerfully as Grandma-san had taught him to do.

Sam left the shrine and saw that his father must be home from work. The car was parked near the electric lantern hanging above the lanai behind their home. He hurried to meet his sister, Grace, who was placing a single water lily in a glass bowl on the dark polished wood of the dining table. Sam looked questioningly at the table, set with only three place mats.

"Papa-san and Mama-san are going to an Aloha dinner," Grace said.

"Is someone coming to Kauai or is someone leaving?" Sam asked. Aloha could mean either a welcome "hello" or a regretful "good-by."

His sister's pretty slanted eyes twinkled with excitement. "I only know that it is a very important dinner," she said. "Papa-san is wearing his best suit and Mama-san is wearing her new brocade sheath."

Sam whistled. It must be an important dinner if his father and mother were going alone and were dressing up on this warm night. Usually the whole family went to things together. They attended a luau or fished or swam together. They went to outdoor music concerts and sat together on a blanket under the stars. What dinner could be so important that he and Grace and Grandma-san were to be left at home?

Sam's father came from the bedroom and went to the kitchen door to speak to Grandma-san. With short running steps she hurried to meet him. The knot of gray hair atop her small head was scarcely as high as his chin. Sam saw how proudly Grandma-san looked at her grown son.

"Mama-san," Sam's father said to her, "we go to the inn to honor the first representative from Hawaii to go to the legislature."

Grandma-san nodded gravely.

Sam knew his father was doing exactly as one should do when he left the house. Sam had been taught this same filial piety; to tell his mother where he was going and why. When he returned he must show himself before her again and ask how she had been in his absence.

"You speak of the lee-gis-la-ture in Honolulu?" Grandma-san asked, carefully emphasizing the vowels in the English words.

"No," her son said. "Our representative goes to the United States to Washington, D. C., itself. Hawaii is a state now, remember?"

Sam saw that Grandma-san was really impressed. She clapped her hands before her and dipped her head quickly as if her son were the representative himself.

When Papa-san and Mama-san had gone to the car, Grace helped Grandma-san bring to the table a fresh green salad and ice-cold papayas, a melonlike fruit, and the delicious rice balls Sam liked to much. Sam ate all that was put on his plate. He was glad that his father took the trouble to grow the tender rice for Grandma-san, who did not like the rice bought in a store.

Grandma-san leaned forward and heaped Sam's plate again with rice balls. "Eat many," she said. "Already you are smart boy—and strong. By and by, maybe, *you* represent Hawaii in the lee-gis-la-ture in Washington Dee Cee."

KICHAGORO TADIKI

*Kichagoro Tadiki (called Tad)
—Japanese Buddhist. He lives
on the island of Kauai on a sugar
plantation where his father and
grandfather and uncles
and cousins work.*

TAD TADIKI pulled the brim of his baseball cap lower
over his tanned yellow forehead to shade his eyes from the
morning sun. He put his baseball bat and glove in a corner of
the lanai nearest the door where he could grab them on the run
when he returned from his weekly meditation at the Buddhist
temple. His team was playing today against Captain Danny
O'Brien's team on the island of Maui.

Tad walked along a narrow road between fields of waving
sugar cane that grew twice his height. He could smell the cane
which yesterday he had helped his father burn over to make
the stalks ready for harvesting.

He liked the excitement of burning the sugar cane. The fire
had to be tended carefully. Only the long ribbon leaves were
burned off quickly to leave the tall sugar canes blackened but
unharmed. After the burning, the stalks were easier to cut and
stack on trucks or on the small cars of the little sugar train
which ran on narrow tracks through the field.

When Tad rode the sugar train with his father and heard
its shrill warning whistle as it chugged through the fields to
carry the cane to the sugar mill, he knew what he wanted to do
when he grew up. He wanted to live and work right here on
the sugar plantation where all his family worked; and he

wanted to play baseball and football on the plantation teams when the day's work was done.

The road through the fields of sugar cane grew steeper, then ended where the irrigation ditches circled the foot of the mountain. On the slope above the sugar cane, which needed a great deal of water, pineapple plants grew in the drier red soil, like a belt around the middle of the mountain. Tad cut through a field of newly set gray-green pineapple plants to the highway and the Buddhist temple in the town.

As Tad entered the temple courtyard, he sniffed the fragrance of the waxy-white blooms of the plumeria bushes bordering the green, well-kept lawn. The temple's coral sand walls were as white as the flowers.

Tad knew that the Buddhist temple was much more splendid than the Shinto shrine where his friend, Sam Yoshido, went to meditate or think. And Buddhism required Tad to learn many more rules for living than Sam had to learn.

But, Tad thought, Buddhists enjoy festivals which Shinto worshipers do not have. Buddhists celebrate gay bon dances in the courtyard when they remember and honor their relatives who are no longer on earth. Then they wear traditional kimonos and dance for joy under the light of gay paper lanterns. For Buddhists believe that death is only the beginning of another life. When one is reborn, he will be wiser and happier in the next life, providing he has followed the eightfold path in his previous life.

Tad swept off his baseball cap and entered the temple. He tiptoed down the aisle past the benches and knelt on the woven grass matting before the altar rail among a dozen boys who were already meditating, or thinking, there.

The beauty of the altar filled him with pleasure. Each article was a symbol to remind him of the teachings of Buddha: the red velvet and gold hangings, flowers, candles and the Buddha image.

Tad looked at the image carved many years ago by a Buddhist monk who had polished the dark wood until it shone like satin. The expression on the face of the Buddha was a mixture of love, compassion, wisdom and peace.

Tad remembered what he had been taught. Looking upon the image of Buddha was not idol worship. He gazed upon the image to be reminded of the truths Buddha had taught, and of the gentleness of the "Enlightened One."

Tad knew that Buddhism was a very old religion. More than two thousand years ago the first Buddha was born a prince, the son of the king and queen of the Sakya Kingdom of India. When the young prince grew up and saw how much selfishness and suffering there were in the world, he gave up his kingdom and went about among the people. He taught them the truths that had come to him while he mediatated under a Bo tree, the tree of wisdom.

Tad began to pray. He did not ask for anything from a divine spirit as his Christian friends did. For him prayer was thinking of the truths taught by Buddha. Today Tad was so excited about the ball game and the airplane ride to Maui that he had difficulty remembering the eight steps in the path to a good life.

He began to check the steps on his fingers: happiness comes from unselfishness; one's words must always be kind and true, never angry; thoughts can change one's whole life, for good thoughts make a good man but evil thoughts make an evil man; in meditation one must make his body and mind quiet.

Tad stopped counting on his fingers and sat very still. He believed that he would understand the true needs of his life if he thought long and quietly. He hoped that sometime in one of his future lives he would reach Nirvana, complete unselfishness and joy through peace of mind.

He could reach Nirvana only through his *own* efforts. This was the law of Karma: what a man sows, he will reap. His life will be as happy as he makes it by living as a true brother to men.

"I must never hate," Tad reminded himself, "for all men are my brothers no matter what their color or religion. I must have the same feelings for the low as for the high, for this is the oneness of life, that the same stream of life runs through all things."

At the end of the hour a gong sounded. Tad stood up with the other boys to leave the temple. From another room in the building he heard the voices of a class of small children singing. Tad knew they had borrowed the tune from a hymn sung by their friends in the Methodist church across the street. Buddhism was an old religion. It had borrowed from many religions over the years, and other religions had borrowed from it. It had adopted a love of beauty from Shintoism and a love of knowledge from Confucianism.

Yet many of the Buddhist beliefs were not borrowed but happened to be similar to those of other religions. Tad thought particularly of the flowers and lighted candles on the altar. Flowers were a symbol of purity. Candles symbolized the Light of Buddha's teaching shining through the dark ignorance of the world. Even the Zuzu, a string of beads similar to the Rosary of his Catholic friends, was a symbol as old as Buddhism. Buddha had told one of his followers who could not remember the many laws, "Make a string of beads and keep them with you. Then you will always be reminded of the Buddha and his teachings."

Tad walked quietly up the aisle, leading the other boys who had knelt with him. When they reached the courtyard Tad and the boys who were on his baseball team saw their coach leaving the Methodist church.

A few years ago coach Jim Kalama had been a football and baseball star at Kamehameha school. He waved and told the boys to hurry. "Wiki-wiki. That plane won't wait for us."

"Meet you at the airport," the boys shouted, walking backward until Pedro Carlos caught up with them from the direction of the Catholic church. Around the corner they found Herb Ching waiting for them in front of the Mormon building.

Almost as soon as they had gathered, the boys scattered to their homes to pick up their baseball equipment.

On the lanai with his bat and glove, Tad found a bag of flat rice cakes which his mother had made to keep him from getting too hungry on the trip. Tad knew from experience that, after the game, the Maui team would treat its visitors to hot dogs, sodas and ice cream.

Carrying the bat over his shoulder, the glove on one hand and the bag of rice cakes in the other, Tad ran back through the sugar cane to the highway and waited for the pickup truck. Sam Yoshida's father had offered to pick up all the boys in the area and take them to the airport. Tad could hear the truckload of boys singing even before he saw Mr. Yoshida's nursery truck coming.

A dozen boys stood in the back of the open-topped truck. Jamie Kohala, who never went anywhere without his ukulele, bent his head over it as if he were trying to hear his own strumming above the lusty voices of the singers.

The truck stopped. Tad stepped on the wheel, caught Sam's outstretched hand and swung over the top rail. He began to sing with the others, "Take me out to the ball game."

A car passed the truck and the driver leaned out the window and called, "Good luck—have fun!"

Children stopped playing in their yards when they saw the truck pass. They waved and shouted, "Have fun." Everyone wanted the team from the sugar plantation to win.

The boys waved to the children and to everyone they saw. They exchanged food they had brought from their homes. Tad shared his rice cakes. Herb Ching passed sweet-sour seed. Pedro broke his Portuguese sweet loaf into chunks. Someone else passed chewing gum. Tad ate until he was thirsty, but he knew there would be plenty of fresh sweet pineapple juice served free by the stewardess on the plane.

Eating, singing and laughing together, the boys rode through the sugar-cane and pineapple fields on their way to the airport to take the plane for Maui, where they would play hard to win the baseball game.

KIM FONG

Kim Fong—Chinese Confucianist. He lives on the island of Maui, helps his father, who guides campers to the crater within the summit of the extinct volcano, Haleakala.

KIM FONG was digging a trench around one of the tents he and his father had put up, when he heard the sound of horses' hoofs sliding on the loose lava rock. He looked up to see four haole men and a boy riding single file down the steep trail which wound from the summit of Haleakala into its crater. Kim waved to the boy. Steve McClure had come with his father from Honolulu.

Steve waved back and shouted, "Hung Hee Fat Choy!"

Kim grinned. The Chinese lunar new year had passed months ago, but the two boys had met at this important Chinese celebration when Kim visited Honolulu to pay his respects to his grandparents there. Kim had taught Steve the Chinese New Year greeting then.

"Hung Hee Fat Choy to you, too!" Kim answered as Steve reigned his horse and slid to the ground.

The boys laughed as if they had said something very funny. "Are you going with the men to take the pictures?" Kim asked.

"No," Steve said, tethering his horse. "I want to explore."

The boys watched the men leave on horseback to photograph

the Silver Sword plants which grow only in Haleakala crater.

Steve turned to Kim. "Wouldn't you like to find a secret burial cave of the old Hawaiian Chiefs?" he asked. "Maybe we'd find relics like the ones we saw in the Bishop Museum."

"I have to finish setting up camp first," Kim said.

"I'll help," Steve offered.

When the boys had completed the trench to keep the tents from flooding if one of the frequent sudden rains came, they climbed a cinder cone nearby. From its top they looked out over the crater valley.

"Do you know where the old burial places were?" Steve asked.

Kim shook his head. As number-one son, Kim often helped his father cook for exploring parties on weekends. The money they earned was saved for the day when Kim would go to college and learn to be a lawyer like his youngest uncle. But there was a loneliness about the great dead volcano pit which had kept Kim from going very far from camp by himself.

"I don't thing the scientists left many of the secrets of the old Hawaiian Chiefs," Kim said. "Unless they missed some of the caves in the cliffs around here."

Steve looked across the width of the crater to the fiery-colored cliffs rimming the valley.

"Haleakala, House of the Sun," Steve said. "My father told me this crater is so deep and wide it forms its own weather in the 'pit.' "

"I've stood at the summit on that rim of cliffs," Kim said, "and watched rain down here in the crater and seen a rainbow form below me while the sun shone about me on the brink."

"I knew Haleakala crater was twenty-seven miles around and more than two thousand feet deep," Steve said, "but I still didn't realize it would be so big or so quiet."

For a moment the boys stood as if listening to the silence. Small plateaus jutted from the towering cliffs at different levels above the floor of the crater. Trees, flowers and grass grew among crags and masses of twisted lava rock which had been hurled as red-hot lava from the crater's core thousands of years before.

Suddenly a trade wind laden with moisture poured through the cliffs of great Koolau Gap in the eastern rim of the crater. The boys jumped, then laughed at each other. Even wind sounded strange and frightening in the remote world within the summit of the mountain.

"Look," Kim cried. "Isn't that a cave below, under that blue-shadowed cliff?"

"Come on," Steve called. "Maybe it's a cave the scientists didn't find!"

The boys slid down the steep side of the cinder cone, but the cave proved to be only the black mouth of an ancient crumbling lava tube. They sat down to empty their sandals of cinder ash. A big drop of rain splashed on the rock in front of them. Kim looked up at the blue bowl of sky overhead and saw the sun disappear behind smoke-colored clouds. Seconds later a downpour of rain sent the boys scurrying into the cover of the shallow lava tube.

"It's a good thing we trenched the tents," Steve said.

Kim nodded. The dark clouds had filled the valley of the crater. It looked as if the storm might last for a while. There was nothing to do but wait here until the wind and rain stopped.

"If we were Hawaiians of long ago," Steve said, "we would think this storm was sent by angry Gods to show us that it was kapu for anyone but chiefs to camp in the House of the Sun."

Kim smiled. "We might even think the friendly God Maui was warning us," he said. "You know Maui was supposed to have stood on top of Haleakala and lassoed the sun to force it to pass more slowly and give the island more sunlight."

"We could use a little of Maui's sunlight right now," Steve said.

A stream of water poured from the rocks overhead to make a curtain across the mouth of the lava tube. In the gloom behind the rain-made waterfall, the boys had barely enough room to sit side by side. They were silent for a few minutes as if they had run out of things to say.

Then Steve said, "In school we're studying religions. That's how I learned about the ancient Hawaiian gods. Next Friday I have to make a report on Confucianism. Tell me, Kim, what you believe—just the most important things."

"Do you have to *write* your report or *tell* it?" Kim asked.

Steve looked surprised and Kim grinned. "You don't want me to tell *too* much if you have to *write* it," he said.

"I have to tell it and write it, both." Steve laughed. "Each one in the class is reporting on one religion in Hawaii. Later we'll write about the most important ideas in each religion to make a scrapbook to keep in our school library. We're clipping pictures of churches from newspapers to illustrate our scrapbooks."

"I'd like to help," Kim said, frowning, "but it isn't easy to think what to say."

"You're planning to be a lawyer," Steve urged. "You ought to be able to explain your ideas better than most of us."

"Well," Kim began, "the most important thing Confucius taught was how to get along with other people. He called it harmony. He said we need rules for living if we want to co-operate with other people.

"Confucius taught most of these rules through the classics —stories describing the old customs and manners of China. He had great respect for the ancient Chinese. He wanted all Chinese people to live up to the best in their past as told in history. He even taught rules to help families live together smoothly."

Steve nodded. "I know about the rules of filial piety," he said. "We have Chinese Christian neighbors and even they seem happier because they follow these rules."

"I almost forgot," Kim said. "Confucius wasn't a savior like the Christ you worship. Confucius was only a wise thinker and a great teacher. Like the Buddha, whose teachings many Chinese follow, Confucius lived and taught more than five hundred years before Christ was born.

"Buddha's teachings spread from India to China. But Confucius was one of our own Chinese people, our greatest scholar and teacher. He based his teachings on the ancient Chinese idea of a superior man."

"You mean a bigger, stronger man?" Steve asked.

"No," Kim answered. "Confucius said that a superior man was a noble man, a princely man. He said that *anyone* at *any time* could live as a princely man if he wanted to.

"Confucius said that people were naturally good. If a man practices doing the right thing, it will become a habit; he will do what is right without even stopping to think."

Steve looked thoughtful. "Getting the right habits in the first place is the hard part, I guess," he said.

"Confucius taught men how to gain and keep good habits, too," Kim said. "He said the natural goodness and love within us will grow if we are helpful to others. And he said, 'Do not do unto others what you would not that they should do unto you.'"

"That sounds like another way of saying the Golden Rule," Steve said.

"Confucius taught five important rules to help *anyone* grow into a superior man," Kim said. "Do you want to hear them, too?"

"Sure," Steve said. "They'll make my report more interesting."

"All right," Kim said and drew a deep breath as if he meant to make a long speech. "Confucious said the superior man will practice the Five Constant Virtues until they are as natural as breathing. The superior man wants to live in harmony with other men. He wants to be kind and helpful. He studies the right way to act in all circumstances and tries to practice good manners and self-control.

"He plans his education so he will know all he can about

history, literature, government and music as well as the knowledge needed to make a living, for the educated man knows how
to take his place in the world.

"He must do what is right no matter what others think
or do, but he must not think unkindly of those who do not think
and act as he does.

"After a man has learned these virtues, he must always try
to practice them," Kim ended.

Steve wiped his forehead with his arm. "That's a tall order!
Do you always follow the five rules?"

Kim grinned. "Confucius said that even he sometimes made
mistakes, but every person grows better by *trying*."

While the boys talked, the cloudburst had stopped. Now
the sun came out as suddenly as it had disappeared. The boys
crawled from the mouth of the lava tube.

Everything about them seemed drowned. The porous lava
rock oozed with water. Ferns and trees were bent with it. Small
streams had formed in every crevice, rushing downhill toward
the floor of the crate. Foaming torrents of water leaped over
cliffs to fall with a roar onto boulders hundreds of feet below.

"This crater valley sure isn't silent now," Steve said, "but
it's even more beautiful."

Kim thought so, too. With the sun glittering on the raindrops
and on the fiery cliffs and tangled fern and creepers, he could
almost imagine himself in Old Hawaii when only great chiefs
were allowed to come into the crater of the House of the Sun.

Kim wished he didn't have to tell Steve that they would
have to go back to camp now. But his father counted on him
to have things ready when the men returned.

"We'll have to leave our exploring until tomorrow," Kim
said. "The trenching we did couldn't keep that cloudburst
from flooding our tents. We'll have to spread the bedrolls in
the sun to dry."

"Come on then," Steve said. "After we dry the blankets, I
sure would like something to eat."

"Coming up—velly soon!" Kim said, holding a hand palm-up above his shoulder as if he carried a platter of food.

The boys laughed and began to climb the slope of the cinder cone together.

CHRIS ABDALONIM

Chris Abdalonim—Arabian-Hawaiian. He lives on a ranch on the big island of Hawaii; helps his grandfather, a Moslem, to train horses.

CHRIS ABDALONIM looked at the newborn colt lying on the grass in a corner of the small corral. She seemed little larger than his dog and her cream-colored sides heaved.

"Is she all right?" Chris asked his grandfather, who stood beside the colt's mother and stroked her long white mane.

The colt gave a sudden kick, scrambled to her feet, took a few wobbly steps and almost ran into Chris. Chris felt tingles move up and down his body as he touched the forehead of the beautiful colt his grandfather had promised to give him for helping with the horses.

"All right?" His grandfather laughed. "Look how frisky she is."

Sunshine, the mother, stretched her neck and nuzzled the colt's nose with hers, and whinnied encouragingly. The colt switched her tail and shook her head and crowded close to Sunshine's side.

"What are you going to name her?" his grandfather asked.

"I haven't decided yet," Chris said. Nothing he could think of seemed good enough for the first colt he had ever owned.

Then Chris saw that Sunshine was trembling. She moved between him and the colt. Her eyes rolled and her nostrils flared.

"There girl—there," his grandfather said soothingly and

patted her shoulder. Then he said to Chris, "The wind has changed. She smells the cinders and smoke from the volcano eruption."

"That volcano is miles away," Chris said to her. "Don't be so skitterish."

Sunshine snorted. The colt slipped under her mother's body as if she wanted a safe roof over her.

Chris laughed. "You're so little, I'll call you Liilii until I can think of a better name," he said.

"A mare likes quiet when her colt is young," his grandfather said. "We'd better leave."

As Chris helped his grandfather with the evening chores, he tried to think of the right name for his colt. Like Sunshine, Liilii was cream-colored with white mane and tail and fringe above the hoofs. She looked like the first beautiful stallion Grandfather had delivered to this ranch from far-off Arabia many years ago when he was a young man. The ranch owner had promised that he could always keep horses of his own if he would remain on the ranch to train the thoroughbred colts. Grandfather had lived here now for forty years.

The next morning Chris was out of bed at dawn. Without waiting for breakfast, he ran to the corral. He stopped at the gate, then turned and ran to his grandfather.

"Sunshine and Liilii are gone," he cried as he woke the old man. "A fence post is pushed over. They must have squeezed through the opening."

Quickly his grandfather dressed. They hurried to the barns and saddled Grandfather's black horse and a spotted pony for Chris.

"We'll pick up their tracks at the break in the fence," Grandfather said when they had mounted. "Wiki-wiki. It is hot out on the plains for such a liilii colt."

For a mile or so they were able to see Sunshine's hoofprints and the smaller marks made by her colt in the gray sand. Then they came to hard lava rock and the hoofprints ended.

"We'd better separate," Grandfather said. "You go to the right through the cactus plains. I'll follow the trail around the hills. We'll meet at the spring in the coconut grove by the sea. She'll probably head that way for water."

Chris rode into the flat cactus country. He lifted his lasso to make sure it wasn't tangled. He knew if he could get the rope on the runaway mare, her colt would follow.

He kept calling, "E-ya! E-ya, there!" If Sunshine and Liilii were hiding behind one of the tall cactus or shrubs, he wanted to startle them into showing themselves.

The sun was hot and there was no breeze today from the sea or from the wet green ranges of the Kohala mountains, which he could see away to his left. Finally Chris stopped to rest his pony and take a drink from his canteen. He leaned forward and poured a little water over his pony's nose.

Chris stood up in the saddle stirrups to see farther across the endless sweep of cactus and cinder cones. Nothing moved. Then a mongoose scurried under his pony. She shied and almost unseated Chris. He decided to cut across the plains toward the coconut grove by the sea where he was to meet his grandfather. He hoped the old man had already found Sunshine and Liilii and was waiting there with them.

A half hour later Chris rode over a rise and saw a long river of cattle moving along a trail which led to the village harbor. Horsemen rode at the edges of the herd, guiding it to the cattle boats for the market in Honolulu.

As Chris rode nearer the herd, the pounding of hoofs and bawling of cattle almost drowned the cries of "Aloha" from the riders who recognized him.

The cowboys rode by, laughing and waving their lassos.

"Aloha," he shouted in return. He didn't ask the men if they had seen Sunshine. She would never bring her colt near a herd, but would hunt a secret safe place to hide.

When he reached the coconut grove, Chris was disappointed not to find his grandfather waiting near the spring with Sunshine and Liilii. He slid from the saddle and while the pony drank, bent to wash his hot face at the spring.

Chris stood up, refreshed. As he looked toward the sea he saw his grandfather. The old man was kneeling in prayer on the black sand beach, looking over the water in the direction he believed the faraway town of Mecca to be; just as he had done five times a day all the years of his life.

Chris knew that his grandfather was saying, "There is no God but Allah and Mohammed is the prophet."

Chris sat down under a coconut palm to wait until his grandfather finished his prayers. He picked three strands of a green vine growing nearby and began to braid them into a lei to put around his colt's neck when he found her.

While his fingers were busy, Chris thought of how troubled he had been when he first realized that his grandfather's religion, Islam, was different from the religions of all the other people who worked on the ranch.

Chris himself went to the Episcopal church in the village with his Hawaiian grandmother and his mother and father. He had been about eight years old when a boy in Sunday school had asked Chris why his grandfather was a Moslem. Until that time Chris had thought nothing of the fact that his grandfather prayed facing Mecca across the world in Saudi Arabia; or that his grandfather's day of rest was Friday instead of Sunday.

After the boy's question, Chris had worried because his grandfather didn't go to one of the Protestant or Buddhist or Catholic churches in the village. His grandfather seemed to be all alone in his strange faith.

Then one day he and his grandfather had watched an old movie on television, in which Arabs and Christians fought on the desert. His grandfather saw how troubled Chris was. He asked Chris to come and sit under a eucalyptus tree beside the corral. Then the old man told him about Allah and the prophet Mohammed.

"Allah is only a different name for the one God," his grandfather said.

"Then why," Chris asked, "did the Arabs on TV call the haoles 'Christian dogs'?"

"Many Moslems used to believe that it was their duty to spread the Islam religion, even if they had to use war to force their beliefs on unbelievers," his grandfather explained.

"You see, when Mohammed lived, six hundred years after Christ, the Arabs were scattered in tribes over the desert as the Indians once lived on the Western Plains of the United States. The Arab tribes were always warring with one another. The Arabs worshiped many gods, one for each day of the year. All the tribes made pilgrimages to the shrine at Mecca where the Black Stone, fallen from Paradise, was kept in a square stone building. Even here the tribes fought over which of their gods should be the favorite.

"Mohammed saw his people quarrel and fight over petty differences. He was wiser and more thoughtful than most men. He knew that their fighting kept the Arabs so weak and divided that they would be helpless if a foreign enemy attacked them.

"Mohammed was a caravan leader and he had traveled to many far places. He had visited cities of the Jews and the Christians where he heard of the one God. He often thought about this God.

"One dark night Mohammed left the city of Mecca, where his people were fighting about the shrine. He was troubled and he went into a cave on the slopes of Mount Hira to meditate. Late in the night he had a vision. He saw the angel Gabriel appear. The angel told Mohammed to join all his scattered people together into one nation which should worship the one God, Allah.

"Mohammed was frightened and thought he must be dreaming. He did not feel that he was good enough to lead his people. He thought about this dream for three years. Then he began to go about, telling the Arabs what Allah had revealed to him through the angel.

"Mohammed said that he was a prophet of God just as Moses had been. He said there was a book in Heaven in which all truth was written. Part of the truth in the book of Heaven had already been revealed to the world by the Jews and Christians. But he, Mohammed, had more truth to tell. Allah had revealed new truth to him.

"Many of the Arabs laughed at Mohammed, but others believed him and followed him. Mohammed was so sure that

Allah wanted him to unite the Arab people into one nation which would worship the one God that he used his armies to overcome unbelieving tribes. He converted them by force; *then* he was kind and helpful to them.

"After many years Mohammed succeeded in uniting the Arab tribes into the strong nation of Arabia. He was pleased to see his people worship Allah instead of idols.

"When Mohammed was an old man, he told his followers in a last sermon, that they must remember to treat all men as brothers. They must help one another. They must be kind to strangers and loyal to friends."

During the four years since Grandfather had told the story of Mohammed, Chris had had plenty of time to observe that his grandfather was liked and respected by the other men on the ranch. His grandfather visited with the Chinese cook and the Japanese gardeners. He sang songs with the Hawaiian and Portuguese and haole cowboys when they gathered in the evening with their ukuleles. He could even dance a comic hula at the ranch luaus.

Yes, Grandfather was well liked even if the old man did worship God in a different way.

Chris finished braiding the vines and tied the ends to form a lei. He looked up and saw his grandfather coming.

"You want to see a real happy colt?" his grandfather called.

Chris stood up. "Did you find Sunshine and Liilii?"

His grandfather smiled. "They are hidden behind that cliff," he said. "There's a pocket above a cove. It's smaller than the corral, with plenty of grass and trees, a real hideaway."

"Can we lasso Sunshine among the trees?" Chris asked.

"No," the old man said. "I've been waiting for you to slip down over the cliff and put a rope on her if you can."

Chris ran up the slope ahead of his grandfather. When he reached the top of the cliff, he saw Sunshine cropping the lush green grass. The colt was frisking about in the miniature valley as if the sun and sea and blue skies made her happy to be alive.

His grandfather joined Chris, puffing for breath. "I never saw a sassier, happier colt," he said.

Chris started down the hill toward Sunshine.

"Take it easy," his grandfather cautioned.

Chris moved forward slowly with a rope and the vine lei over his arm. Sunshine raised her head and whinnied. He spoke gently to her as he had heard his grandfather do. "There-girl-there."

The colt pricked up her ears and ran under her mother. Chris moved nearer to them, talking all the while. "I won't hurt you. See, I made this lei for you. Come let me put it on you."

The soothing words, the warmth and quiet place seemed to calm Sunshine. She tossed her head but she didn't run when Chris slipped the rope around her neck. The colt grew brave enough to come from under her mother and prance stiff-legged around Chris.

He held out the lei. She was so curious that she came near enough to nose it. Chris dropped the lei around her neck.

The colt whirled and raced off across the grassy slope to the water's edge. A breaker roared into the cove to meet the colt. She brought herself up so short that her hind legs slid under her body and she almost sat down on the black sand.

Chris laughed until the tears ran down his cheeks. He could hear his grandfather laughing from the cliff above. The colt dashed back to her mother, tossing her head and tangling the green lei in her white mane.

"She's really having fun," Chris called.

"Yes, she is lealea — one happy colt," his grandfather answered.

"Lealea! That's what I'll call her," Chris shouted. "Liilii-Lealea. Little-Happy."

He knew that he had found just the right name for his frisky colt. And when she was grown, he would shorten her name to Lealea.

Chris lead Sunshine up the slope. "Come on Liilii-Lealea," he called. "It's a long way home."

DARA MALWAR

Dara Malwar—Hindu visitor to Hawaii from India. He lives at one of the hotels at Waikiki in Honolulu on the island of Oahu while his father attends a summer session at the University of Hawaii.

DARA MALWAR ran from the hotel cottage along a winding path through flowering bushes to Waikiki beach. He wanted a swim before breakfast. The early sun had turned Diamond Head to a great cliff of gold rising above the blue-green water. Dara raced across the white sand and dived into a warm breaker. Caught by a backwash, he tumbled over and over until he was left, standing waist-deep, in a trough between the foaming waves.

He laughed and shook the wet black hair from his forehead. His father was attending the East-West Philosophers' Conference at the University of Hawaii. When Dara came with him to Hawaii six weeks ago, he wouldn't have dared go into water as rough as this. He had learned to swim in a pool in the garden of his home in India. He had never even seen heaving mountains of water roll toward shore with the furious speed of these waves, and he hadn't dreamed that swimming could be such fun.

Now, Dara thought, maybe I could pass the swim test to sail an El Toro. A boy or girl had to be an excellent swimmer to be allowed to set foot in the little one-man racing rigs. Early in the summer his friend Jimmy had told Dara, "Ya gotta be able to take care of yourself if the boat flips."

Dara felt sure he could handle himself safely in water now, but he was going back to India with his father in a few hours.

Dara dived into a breaker racing toward him and turned on his back to be carried to shore. He scrambled up the beach and joined his father at a table on the open-air lanai of the hotel.

"Good morning, Father," he said. "Do I have time to go to the Ala Wai yacht harbor to tell Jimmy and the other boys good-by? They'll be there practicing for the El Toro races."

Dara's father looked young when he smiled and his teeth seemed very white in contrast to his dark skin.

"Don't be long," he said. "I promised we'd stop at the university before we went to the airport and tell our friends there good-by."

As the pretty Japanese waitress brought his breakfast, Dara saw a myna bird hop onto the low stone beach wall. He tossed crumbs from his pancakes and smiled when the bird fluttered to the grass to eat them. In India each morning he fed the birds before he ate to remind him to share with all creatures from the lowest insect to the highest man.

After breakfast Dara ran to the cottage to dress. He found that the houseboy had already come for their baggage and sent it to the airport. Dara's travel clothes lay on the bed. He dressed and was soon walking the top of the beach wall toward Ala Wai harbor. He wished his mother and sister and family guru, teacher, could see how much at home he was on this island and how many friends he had made.

Before Dara left India, his mother had been anxious about his leaving home for the first time on a trip to a foreign land. His father would be busy attending classes and conferences and lectures. But his father had said that it was time for Dara to learn to feel at home in any place. Dara could speak English. He planned to go to a college in the United States as his father had done. This trip would be a good experience for him.

"The Hawaiian Islands are the crossroads between the East and the West," his father had told his mother. "Dara will be with people of every nationality and religion. And he is old enough to remember the great men from all over the world who will attend the East-West Philosophers' Conference. He can go with me to the public lectures."

Dara's mother had gone, then, to show the servants what to pack for him. She knew that her son, born into the honored Brahmin caste, had a responsibility to become a leader when he was grown, and to teach those in other castes.

"I will miss you," she told Dara, "but your father is right. You must seek wisdom and knowledge wherever it is to be found. Even a woman knows that the most important part of anyone is the spirit."

Dara's guru, who had instructed him in the ancient wisdom of India, reminded him, too, to learn all he could in the foreign land.

"Cows are of many different colors, but milk is alike," his teacher told Dara as he said good-by. "You will meet men of many different faiths, but each of them looks to OM, the one Brahman, the highest One."

Now, ahead of him, Dara saw the Ala Wai harbor and the many colored sails of the little skiff-like El Toros rocking in the stiff breeze. He ran along the shore and waved to his friends, who were practice-sailing.

Eli, under yellow sail, heaved to and sailed within inches of the dock where Dara stopped. "Aloha," he shouted. "Come next year, Dara. I'll let you sail my boat."

Steve sailed by and called, "Aloha, Dara."

Then Dara saw the red and blue striped sails of Jimmy's boat weaving in and out among the other El Toros. Dara thought no one else could sail a boat as skillfully as his strong Hawaiian friend, or swim as much like a fish.

Dara had met Jimmy Mahiai at the Ala Wai soon after he came to Honolulu. He had gone for a walk and stopped here on the dock feeling a little homesick. The Hawaiian boy had been stepping into his boat and he called to Dara. "Hey there —you sail El Toro, too?"

From that moment the boys had been friends. Dara would never forget his surprise the first time Jimmy took him to his home, a sprawling old house behind the vegetable and lei market which Jimmy's mother owned.

For years Mrs. Mahiai had taken into her home, and to her warm heart, any neighborhood boy or girl who needed a home. Jimmy's adopted brothers and sisters were not only of several ages and sizes, but also of different nationalities.

He had a Chinese sister, a Japanese-Spanish sister, a brother who was Hawaiian-Scottish and a French-Hawaiian baby brother, as well as his real sister, Evalani.

In Jimmy's home, where everyone was treated alike, Dara helped wash dishes for the first time in his life. He fed the pet rabbits, and sang Hawaiian songs with the other children accompanied by Jimmy's ukulele.

Dara ran to meet Jimmy, who was tying his El Toro to the dock. Jimmy turned with a friendly grin. "You must go now?" he asked.

Dara nodded. He had come here to say good-by but, face to face with the friend he liked best, he could only swallow.

"The thing I'd like mos'," Jimmy said in his own soft way of speaking, "is for you to stay right here. Maybe your papa come back next year—and you, too?"

"I hope so," Dara said.

Dara saw Jimmy's sister, Evalani, battling to raise the sail on an El Toro. "Maybe we ought to help Evalani," he said. "That wind is strong."

"Bettah she learn to do it herself," Jimmy said. "My sistah need help—she'll yell."

His words were so like his easygoing ways that Dara laughed.

"Jimmy," he said, "I'm sure glad I met you. I never knew a family like yours before—all so different but so friendly and good to each other."

Jimmy grinned. "You trying to say—the bes' thing you like mos' in Hawaii—is how the people are all mixed up in a friendly way?"

"I guess that's what I mean," Dara said. "Anyway I think I learned as much from knowing your family as my father learned at the East-West Conference."

"Then bettah you come back next year," Jimmy said.

The two boys looked at each other. Finally Dara said, "Well, my father will be waiting."

"Aloha," Jimmy said.

Dara ran along the beach toward the hotel, turning several times to wave at Jimmy, who was still standing in front of his El Toro.

As Dara and his father rode in a taxi through the tree-shaded streets to the university, Dara hoped that some day the streets of India would be as clean as those in Honolulu. He hoped that a way would be found to feed the many hungry people in his own land so that they would look as healthy and happy as the men and women and children he saw walking along the sidewalks here.

There was only one thing that Dara thought could improve Honolulu. He missed the sleek, friendly cows which roamed the streets in India. At home the cows wandered wherever they wished, into traffic where the cars stopped for them, and into the gardens where children petted them and women gave them grain and fresh vegetables.

The Hindu religion was so old that many of its customs had come from songs and stories told for more than three thousand years. The worship and love of cows was one of these customs. Dara knew that the great man of peace, Mahatma Gandhi, had said that the purpose of cow worship was to teach Hindus to be gentle and kind to animals.

"Many religions teach men to love man," Gandhi had said, "but Hindus love all living things. When we love all living things, we learn to love man more. And the love of man leads us nearer to oneness with Brahman."

When Dara and his father reached the campus of the University of Hawaii, they entered one of the white coral buildings set among flowers and trees and wide lawns. It was pleasantly cool as they walked the long corridor. Along one wall Dara saw an exhibit of paintings and sculpture by artists who lived in Hawaii. Guided by laughter and the buzz of voices, he and his father easily found the room where their friends were gathered. They stopped inside the doorway.

Dara saw that, following the friendly Hawaiian custom, everyone was wearing leis, even the older men with gray hair and much wisdom. Two men came and placed leis around his father's neck, one of red carnations and one of pink. Someone dropped an orchid lei over Dara's head.

"Mahalo nui," he thanked them, and dipped his chin to admire the velvet purple petals against his white shirt.

Dara heard a rapping on a desk and looked up to see a man who he thought might be a teacher trying to gain the attention of the group. Beside the teacher stood two students with notebooks in their hands.

"I know we invited you here for a farewell party," the teacher said, smiling, "but these student reporters will be grateful if you will allow them to ask a few questions for their newspaper and class reports.

"All of us here have listened for several weeks to the ideas of the greatest thinkers of the Orient and of the West. Will you try to sum up, *in a very few words*—" He paused as the men in the room laughed at his emphasis on "a very few words." "Try to sum up," he said again, "the idea you feel is most important to take home with you—and to pass on to others."

The men began to talk again while the student reporters moved among them asking questions and writing down answers. Dara realized that a reporter would soon come to his father and his heart began to beat faster. What would his father choose to say?

He knew that his father admired Ramakrishna, a great Hindu leader who had lived about the same time as America's Abraham Lincoln. Although only one path was required of a man, Ramakrishna had studied and followed all three of the paths by which a person could know Brahman: the way of good deeds, the way of true knowledge of self, and the way of pure devotion and worship.

In addition Ramakrishna had believed that it was important to understand the spiritual values of other religions. "Understanding each other is our hope for peace," he had said. "We must know what other people believe if we are to understand them."

Would his father quote from Ramakrishna's sayings? Dara wondered.

The Hindu leader had said, "As one can ascend to the top of a house by means of a ladder or bamboo or a staircase or a rope, so divers are the ways and means to approach God, and every religion in the world shows one of these ways. Different creeds are but different paths to reach the Almighty."

And Ramakrishna had said, "As a mother, in nursing her sick children, gives rice and curry to one, and sago arrowroot to another and bread and butter to a third, so the Lord has laid out different paths for different men suitable to their nature.

"Dispute not. As you rest firmly on your own faith and opinion, allow others also the equal liberty to stand by their own faiths and opinions."

Dara saw a student reporter stop before his father. With pencil poised above his notebook, the student asked, "Would you say, sir, that the battle of ideas between the Eastern and Western Philosophers has been worth while? Did you discover any likenesses among you?"

Dara thought, Father looks thoughtful even when he smiles.

"In appearance, body and dress, we certainly are *not* alike," his father said, "as you can see if you look around this room. And no one who listened to our long intense discussions this summer can accuse us of *thinking* alike. We still prefer many different ways of living.

"But East or West, we are alike in the spirit-within-us, in that true part of every person for which the body is only a cloak. Each of us seeks in his own way for 'oneness' with the Divine Creator of all men.

"This one way in which we *are alike* gives me hope for the future of mankind. I believe that the seed of mutual understanding which we sowed here will grow and help lead to world peace."

The men nearby clapped, and Dara couldn't help feeling proud. Then his father said good-by to his friends.

The taxi was waiting and his father told the driver that there was barely time to reach the airport to catch their plane. He said to Dara, "When we are on board, the stewardess will place our leis in plastic bags and they should keep fresh until we reach home. Your mother and sister will like them."

Dara thought a moment. "You could give your two leis to them," he said. "I would like to put mine around the neck of the first cow we meet."

His father laughed. "She will probably eat it," he said.

As the taxi pulled up before the airport entrance, they heard their flight number being called on the loudspeaker. They hurried through the building, had their tickets checked at the gate, crossed the runway and climbed the steps into the plane.

They had barely fastened their seat belts when the whine of the jet engines increased. The plane began to rise.

Through the window Dara saw Diamond Head standing high above the beach at Waikiki. He saw the sailboats looking like toys in the harbor, and the city of Honolulu spread out against the backdrop of green mountain peaks. Then he looked down at the airport.

On the tower, spelled in large letters, he saw the word, ALOHA, which meant so many things in Hawaii—hello, I love you, good-by, come back soon.

Dara pressed his nose against the window glass. "Aloha," he called. "Aloha!"

Pronounciation of Hawaiian words used:

Ala Wai	*ah-lah wy-ee*, canal and yacht harbor at Wai-kiki
Alii	*ah-lee-ee*, chief
Aloha	*ah-loh-ha*, love, hello, good-by
Haleakala	*ha-lay-ah-kah-lah*, extinct volcano on island of Maui
haole	*how-lee*, white person, Caucasian
hau	*how*, a tree found in Hawaii
Hawaii	*hah-wy-ee*, the "Big Island" of the Hawaiian chain of islands
Hilo	*hee-low*, largest city on big island of Hawaii
Honolulu	*hoh-no-loo-loo*, capital and largest city of Hawaii on the island of Oahu
huhu	*hoo-hoo*, angry
hukilau	*hoo-kee-lau*, pull-net fishing party
Kamehameha	*kah-may-hah-may-hah*, King who conquered and united the several islands of Hawaii
Kapiolani	*kah-pee-oh-lah-nee*, a chieftess on the big island when the missionaries came to Hawaii
kapu	*kah-poo*, tabu, forbidden
Kauai	*kah-wy-ee*, the "Garden Isle," fourth largest of the Hawaiian chain
Kilauea	*kee-lah-way-ah*, active crater on the slope of volcano Mauna Loa
Kohala	*koh-hah-lah*, mountain on the big island of Hawaii
Lahaina	*lah-hi-nah*, port on Maui and old capital of Hawaii
lanai	*lah-nigh-ee*, open air room or porch
lealea	*lay-ah-lay-ah*, happy
lei	*lay*, long string or loop of flowers, garland
liilii	*lee-ee-lee-ee*, little
luau	*loo-au*, Hawaiian outdoor feast, usually with entertainment

mahalo nui	*mah-hah-low noo-ee,* thanks very much
Maui	*mow-ee,* second largest island of Hawaii
Molokai	*mo-low-ky-ee* one of the islands of Hawaii
muumuu	*moo-moo,* a full unbelted dress, long or short
Oahu	*oh-ah-hoo,* third largest island of Hawaii
Pali	*pah-lee,* cliff over which King Kamehameha forced his enemies and won the island to unite Hawaii
Pele	*pay-lay,* goddess of volcano
plumeria	*plu-may-ree-ah,* flowering large shrub or tree
poi	*poy,* a pastelike food made of flour made by pounding taro root
taro	*tah-row,* large tuberous root like a potato
ukulele	*oo-koo-lay-lee,* small guitar
Waikiki	*wy-kee-kee,* famous beach at Honolulu
wikiwiki	*weekee-weekee,* hurry